Puppy Love

Photographs by Kay McKinley
Words by Susan Ashley

OVER THE FENCE
PUBLISHING

To Kelley, for her patience and joie de vivre,
and to Ben

Over the Fence Publishing
5440 N. Berkeley Blvd.
Milwaukee, WI 53217
E-mail: overthefence@wi.rr.com

ISBN 0-9741856-0-4

Printed in the United States of America

I am a puppy that feels very lucky.

There's so much I love to do.

Sleeping

and snuggling…

Listening and nuzzling…

Do you love these things, too?

Taking first steps

and hearing, "You did it!"

Making up plans

to sneak out – I admit it!

Getting encouraged to go out and explore…

I love all these things and more.

Being brave at the vet

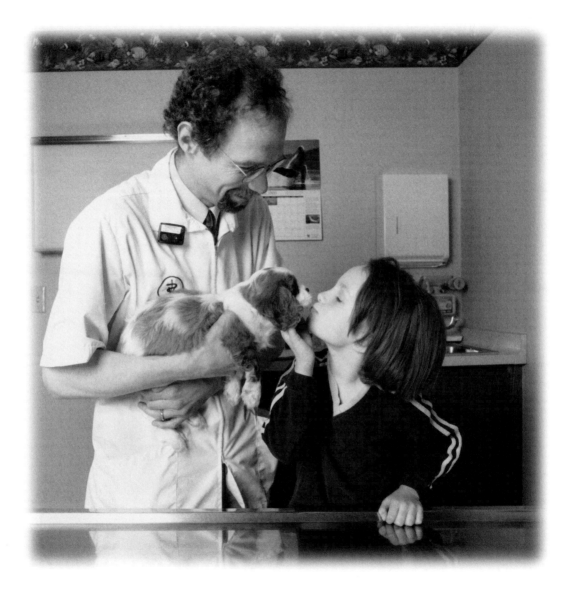

and getting kissed when it's done…

Playing outside

in the bright summer sun…

Running and running

without slowing down…

Getting dressed up

and going out on the town…

Sharing a story before going to bed

and laughing together at things we have read…

Sleeping and dreaming
as stars shine above...

There are so many things
for a puppy to love.